D1596281

ON NOT KNOWING HOW TO LIVE

Books by Allen Wheelis

ON
NOT KNOWING
HOW
TO LIVE

Allen Wheelis

1817

HARPER & ROW, PUBLISHERS

NEW YORK, EVANSTON, SAN FRANCISCO,
LONDON

FIRST EDITION

Designed by Sidney Feinberg

Library of Congress Cataloging in Publication Data

Wheelis, Allen, 1915–
    On not knowing how to live.
    I. Title.
PZ4.W564On [PS3573.H44]   813'.5'4   75-4294
ISBN 0–06–014562–5

75 76 77 78 79 10 9 8 7 6 5 4 3 2 1

80046

for ILSE

Contents

I

THE STRANGER

I HAVE come to a strange land. I do not understand the language. The customs are peculiar.

At home I didn't have to think which path to take. One foot simply followed the other out into an average expectable environment to which I had a built-in adaptability. The unexpected could happen but remained the exception. Unthinking reactions had a natural fit with the way things were. In this land fixed attributes of life have fallen loose and slanted. Familiar things are slightly twisted, have entered another dimension, and no spontaneous reaction of mine fits with anything. I must stay alert. I can never sleep. I have a terrible longing for home.

I am powerfully attracted by their girls. I watch the dark swinging curls as they bend over their work, the delicate features, the mysteriously swelling bosoms. Longing sinks into me like a knife, senses sicken, madness is not far away. Sometimes I think they are attracted to me too, but in an easygoing contented way, nothing like this panic craving.

Yet with all this watching, this jungle of fantasy, I don't really know what I want. To touch and to hold, to possess, to enter . . . but something more. The universe swings in the balance, and all hope of meaning, but whatever it is I know I'm never to have it. My gaze locks on arched lips, on eyes in which for a breathtaking moment invitation flickers, on dark lashes which sweep down over glimpsed secrets. An abyss opens within me, sucks dry my throat. Heels click by on the pavement, skirt sways, brown eyes glance my way—suddenly she turns the corner and is gone, and I see, reflected in a store window, a face of hollow anguish.

How to live? Who knows the question knows not how. Who knows not the question cannot tell.

The way to live must depend both upon what one is and upon the world in which the living will take place. I must concern myself equally with understanding my own nature and the nature of this strange land.

But maybe it is difficult only in its obviousness. Maybe it really is very simple: the way to live is to act. Maybe not knowing how to live means nothing more than being afraid to participate, pulling away to the side, watching life go by without taking that part in it which one would want to take were he not afraid.

To participate is to share an endeavor, to be involved, to interact, hence in some measure to be accountable. Something in me holds back: "No one must have a claim on me," it seems to say; "no one must tug at my coat." And further, "No one must criticize me." And ultimately, "No one must attack or denounce me." Absolute immunity is what I seem to want, and the price is isolation. Maybe not knowing how to live is nothing more than being willing to pay such an exorbitant price.

What fantastic hope nourishes me? That if I suffer this desert long enough I will eventually achieve something of such significance that it will constitute a safe-conduct back to the city of man, and that meanwhile the intensity of my cloistered participation will make up a bit for its distance and indirectness, enough for me to go on, and will bring about eventually a true fulfillment, though perhaps posthumous.

Far removed, alone, I wait for a call that will never come. There is no safe-conduct. The only way back is through risk. Suddenly I remember Jenny.

Jenny and I sit cross-legged on the floor. We are six years old, playing marbles for keeps. Light brown hair curtains her gray eyes and freckled face. She claims a marble not fairly won, I grab her hand, she stands up laughing, we struggle. The struggle becomes unbearably sweet. I cannot give it up. The plains of being are flooded with desire, everything is swept away, I utter in a voice suddenly hoarse the terrible word: "Let's fuck." "All right," she says, and I am astonished at the ease and simplicity with which she immediately lies on the floor, pulls up her dress. I stand above her, look down on treasure suddenly mine, hesitate. An inward glance encounters an invincible prohibition which impales my conscience as heavy spear a leaping fawn. "No . . ." I say, "let's don't." "All right," she says. It's all the same to her, she's a summer day, carefree, wants to play. She stands. Curtains fall back in place over mysterious garden. I am struck by iron remorse, locked in a conflict from which I shall never be free.

What determines what I do? Principle, as I like to think, or faint heart which achieves the same end?

We sat on the ground and leaned against a tree, shoulders touching, fingers intertwining. Children waded in the brook, laughed, mothers called. We took off our shoes, tunnelled our toes under matted needles. The red sun on the horizon palisaded the grove of pines with golden pales. We looked in each other's eyes, talked about ourselves, understood many things. The afternoon was ending, people were leaving. Darkness came. No sounds now but the locusts and the brook, no light but the fireflies—bright periods on the dark page before us. We lay on the ground, and when we talked we whispered. She did not push back my hands, seemed to feel that what I felt was good.

It was late when we came from the park. The houses were dark. From far away came the sound of a speeding car, a whining menace spreading in the still night. Coming from darkness we blinked in the glare of a street light. Thousands of locusts in a teeming halo swarmed about the light, flew against it, fell to the still warm sidewalk.

Through a long hot summer we went often to the park. In August her manner changed, her face darkened. I had forebodings, dreams of losing her. She laughed at my gloom but with a hollow note. Her parents took her away for a vacation. I walked the streets waiting, counted hours, checked off days. When she returned her eyes were swollen; she would not look at me. When finally she told me, I was relieved, had feared something worse. I wanted to marry her but she would not. We found the name of a doctor in another city, invented a story for her parents, went by train.

The waiting room was dirty. A sign on the desk informed us we should ring the bell and wait. We sat on an old sofa which responded with a cloud of dust and the twang of a broken spring. There was but one window, morning sunlight falling on a begrimed pane. The door opened and a Mexican girl came out, glanced at us furtively. Presently the doctor appeared, a heavy man in a surgical gown. With a gesture he invited us in, explained the procedure. "I've found it best," he said, "to collect my fee in advance." I gave him the money which he tucked away under his gown. With sudden helplessness I watched him take her into an inner room. When she came out she walked very slowly. At the hotel we tried to look grown-up, registered under false names, felt like thieves.

She slept for a while, restlessly, talking in her sleep, woke feeling better. The day passed with a terrible slowness. Nothing happened. She telephoned her parents, invented a reason for getting back late. I called the doctor who protested but agreed finally to see her. He did not carry a bag and there was nothing physicianly in his manner. "Spread your legs," he said, pulling on one rubber glove. He lifted her skirt and examined her brusquely, as she stood there by the door. She gasped and clutched the wall. "It'll come," he said. "Just give it time."

But we had no time. Our alibis were used up and we had to go back. Somehow I got her aboard the train and into a lower berth. She kept smiling and saying she was all right, squeezing my hands very hard. The pullman was filling with people preparing for bed. The train began to move. For two more hours she held on and we were almost there when it happened. She writhed and kicked, bumping her head on the underside of the upper berth, falling against the window, clutching the sheets, tearing at her clothes. She dug her fingernails into my arm and into her own face. She bit her tongue and there was blood on her mouth, but she did not cry out. I ran to find a doctor, found no one. When I got back she was gone and the sheet was red. Even in the dim light of the corridor I saw the dark stains on the carpet. An elderly woman putting up her hair in curlers gave a little scream as I entered the ladies' lounge. The toilet door was unlocked and there I found her. She could not hold up her head but the pain was less. A thick cord twisted down from her body through the toilet, out into the night and the wind and the clacking wheels below. I cut it with a razor blade, tied the stump with a shoe string. She fell as I knelt to help her up. The train had reached our destination, the conductor was calling all aboard. I just managed to get her off. She lay on a bench while I telephoned for help, but the doctor said he couldn't get mixed up in anything like that. Then she beckoned to me, said she wanted to go home.

Her parents were asleep and she got in unobserved. I walked about her house till morning, watching her window, telephoned throughout the day. Always she said she was fine, did not want me to visit. On the second day she met me in the park—pale, pale, pale.

Perhaps if I teach others what I know not, I may along the way myself learn. The stranger gives lessons in how to feel at home, helps many people. Passing years bring recognition, even a certain distinction. I must count myself a success. But in the walled depths where I live when others sleep, when rain falls on a deserted island, nothing is changed.

When my last patient leaves I am through and could go home, but lie on the couch, cold, feeling still the warmth of another body, drawing it in. I look out at the sky. The snow has stopped. It is cold and getting colder. A rising wind has cleared the sky, and the leafless tops of elms are touched with thin winter sunshine. I get up finally and go through the routine of leaving: putting on hat and gloves, warm and dry from a day in the steam-heated building; stuffing trouser bottoms into high galoshes; snapping off the light; checking the mailbox in the deserted secretarial office; then down the hall past the popping radiator to the front door and out into the cold.

Main Street is deserted. A few houses have wreaths on the doors, colored lights in the windows. Inside, dinners are being prepared, fires are burning, dogs bark, children play. Outside is the wind. In the hospital, patients are sitting in the lounge, idling at jigsaw puzzles, reading magazines, waiting for the dinner chime. The office building behind me is empty. Everyone has gone home.

The interlacing elm branches brush together in the wind with a dry clicking sound. As I put my hand on the door handle of my car I hear a whispering of clawed feet. High above the street a troop of squirrels, perhaps fifteen or twenty, are scampering through the smallest branches against the pale green sky. They move together, very fast, almost flying, the branches dipping to their weight and swaying in the wind—waves of soft fur fleeing from high branch to high branch, from tree to tree, in a convulsive sinuous writhing. A frantic search for food, I think, a last hopeless expedition for nuts before being caught and held in the vise of winter. I stand there watching until they disappear, my hand on the door handle, the cold seeping through my glove. All is known. What I have done before I may do again. Spring will follow winter. What lies ahead is already past.

"I am now forced to admit," writes Cyril Connolly, "that anxiety is my true condition, occasionally intruded upon by work, pleasure, melancholy or despair."

11

80046

Sam stops me in the hall to chat. He is unfailingly cordial, but is envious, and I hear from others that he speaks disparagingly of me. As we talk I hear in my voice a phony joviality, the sound of fear. I am dismayed.

Fear may serve life when one flees danger, but such fear is brief: one runs away, the fear subsides, one resumes living. Chronic fear cripples, leads to cowering, to the abandonment of our task. Our task is to affirm something, to bear spirit forward.

Yet a way of life originating in fear may come in time to put down roots, to bear distinctive fruit, and to acquire thereby an authenticity superseding its defensive origin. One may find reason to retain a value born of fear even after gaining the courage to lay it aside. Rilke was drawn toward psychoanalysis by neurotic suffering, but turned back. "Can you understand, my friend," he wrote to the analyst, "that I am afraid of disturbing by any classification or survey, be it ever so relieving, a much higher order whose right, after all that has happened, I would have to acknowledge, even if it were to destroy me?" This is treacherous ground, deception lies in wait. One may rationalize loyalty to a limp by persuading oneself it has acquired grace. A much higher order? How can he be sure? What guarantees it? Nothing. And there's no escaping this uncertainty; if you mean it you must affirm it on your own authority, and at your own peril go ahead.

For better or worse my life turns ever more inward, moves further from all that is outward and public. Because I accept it and affirm it this becomes my fate, and it is this to which I bear witness.

My friend Alfred speaks in his ruminative and provocative way of the forthcoming Gifford Lectures which he is to give in Edinburgh: "You know, everybody will be there . . . everybody from the Prime Minister on down. It's such a responsibility." He copes with ambivalence by creating little psychodramas, charms his friends into arguing one or another aspect of his various conflicts, listens in mock court, arrives eventually at his own synthesis. He comes up often in my thoughts in the month of January. I begin the new year by taking the measure of my distance and of my difference from him.

When one becomes a public figure *the* audience becomes *one's* audience—because one has accepted its acclaim and has consented to lead. One enters then an implied contract which requires one to maintain a certain relation with this audience, to continue to occupy for it the position originally taken, not to disappoint, not to shock; and this does indeed become "such a responsibility." One cannot meet this responsibility and remain altogether true to inner vision. The creative impulse begins to look two ways, becomes negotiable, arrives at a compromise between inner vision and the expectations of one's audience. Inner vision is transformed into accommodation, is lost.

I lack both the rewards and the bondage of having an audience. In my life the creative impulse looks but one way, inward, is subject to no restraint, bends to no accommodation, is responsible to no one's expectation. Always the inner vision may be lost, and driveling it away in obligation to an audience, in payment for that audience's esteem, is but one among many ways. Alone on a mountain top it may be lost, may be lost in confusion, in faintness of heart, or by fleeing from loneliness into a spurious belonging. But if I can hold on to what I know I am free to explore it, can make a journey into the interior that a public figure cannot make, and in the travel notes on that dark journey am subject to no restraint.

II

SPIRIT

W E COME into being as a slight thickening at the end of a long thread. Cells proliferate, become an excrescence, assume the shape of a man. The end of the thread now lies buried within, shielded, inviolate. Our task is to bear it forward, pass it on. We flourish for a moment, achieve a bit of singing and dancing, a few memories we would carve in stone, then we wither, twist out of shape. The end of the thread lies now in our children, extends back through us, unbroken, unfathomably into the past. Numberless thickenings have appeared on it, have flourished and have fallen away as we now fall away. Nothing remains but the germ-line. What changes to produce new structures as life evolves is not the momentary excrescence but the hereditary arrangements within the thread.

We are carriers of spirit. We know not how nor why nor where. On our shoulders, in our eyes, in

17

anguished hands through unclear realm, into a future unknown, unknowable, and in continual creation, we bear its full weight. Depends it on us utterly, yet we know it not. We inch it forward with each beat of heart, give to it the work of hand, of mind. We falter, pass it on to our children, lay out our bones, fall away, are lost, forgotten. Spirit passes on, enlarged, enriched, more strange, complex.

We are being used. Should not we know in whose service? To whom, to what, give we unwitting loyalty? What is this quest? Beyond that which we have what could we want? What is spirit?

A river or a rock, writes Jacques Monod, "we know, or believe, to have been molded by the free play of physical forces to which we cannot attribute any design, any 'project' or purpose. Not, that is, if we accept the basic premise of the scientific method, to wit, that nature is *objective* and not *projective*."

That basic premise carries a powerful appeal. For we remember a time, no more than a few generations ago, when the opposite seemed manifest, when the rock *wanted* to fall, the river to sing or to rage. Willful spirits roved the universe, used nature with whim. And we know what gains in understanding and in control have come to us from the adoption of a point of view which holds that natural objects and events are without goal or intention. The rock doesn't *want* anything, the volcano pursues no purpose, river quests not the sea, wind seeks no destination.

But there is another view. The animism of the primitive is not the only alternative to scientific objectivity. This objectivity may be valid for the time spans in which we are accustomed to reckon, yet untrue for spans of enormously greater duration. The proposition that light travels in a straight line, unaffected by adjacent masses, serves us well in surveying our farm, yet makes for error in the mapping of distant galaxies. Likewise, the proposition that nature, what is just "out there," is without purpose, serves us well as we deal with nature in days or years or lifetimes, yet may mislead us on the plains of eternity.

Spirit rises, matter falls. Spirit reaches like a flame, a leap of dancer. Out of the void it creates form like a god, *is* god. Spirit was from the start, though even that beginning may have been an ending of some earlier start. If we look back far enough we arrive at a primal mist wherein spirit is but a restlessness of atoms, a trembling of something there that will not stay in stillness and in cold.

Matter would have the universe a uniform dispersion, motionless, complete. Spirit would have an earth, a heaven and a hell, whirl and conflict, an incandescent sun to drive away the dark, to illumine good and evil, would have thought, memory, desire, would build a stairway of forms increasing in complexity, inclusiveness, to a heaven ever receding above, changing always in configuration, becoming when reached but the way to more distant heavens, the last . . . but there is no last, for spirit tends upward without end, wanders, spirals, dips, but tends ever upward, ruthlessly using lower forms to create higher forms, moving toward ever greater inwardness, consciousness, spontaneity, to an ever greater freedom.

Particles become animate. Spirit leaps aside from matter which tugs forever to pull it down, to make it still. Minute creatures writhe in warm oceans. Ever more complex become the tiny forms which bear for a moment a questing spirit. They come together, touch; spirit is beginning to create love. They touch, something passes. They die, die, die, endlessly. Who shall know the spawnings in the rivers of our past? Who shall count the waltzing grunion on the shores of ancient seas? Who shall hear the unheard poundings of that surf? Who will mourn the rabbits of the plains, the furry tides of lemmings? They die, die, die, but have touched, and something passes. Spirit leaps away, creates new bodies, endlessly, ever more complex vessels to bear spirit forward, pass it on enlarged to those who follow.

Virus becomes bacteria, becomes algae, becomes fern. Thrust of spirit cracks stone, drives up the Douglas fir. Amoeba reaches out soft blunt arms in ceaseless motion to find the world, to know it better, to bring it in, growing larger, questing further, ever more capacious of spirit. Anemone becomes squid, becomes fish; wiggling becomes swimming, becomes crawling; fish becomes slug, becomes lizard; crawling becomes walking, becomes running, becomes flying. Living things reach out to each other, spirit leaps between. Tropism becomes scent, becomes fascination, becomes lust, becomes love. Lizard to fox to monkey to man, in a look, in a word, we come together, touch, die, serve spirit without knowing, carry it forward, pass it on. Ever more winged this spirit, ever greater its leaps. We love someone far away, someone who died long ago.

Natural selection, acting on random accidents in the genetic code, slowly brings about changes in brain structure, hence in what the brain can do. Culture begins with the appearance of a brain capable of language and reason. Thereafter culture acquires autonomy, begins an evolution of its own. The proliferation of tools begets tool-combinations, hence better tools. Weapons become sharper, kill more certainly, at greater distance. Animals are subdued.

Weapons are used then on men; and this warfare, the outcome of which depends on cultural evolution, becomes a new selective pressure affecting biological evolution. For it is men of most enhanced brain capacity who create the most advanced culture, and it is just this culture which creates the deadliest weapons, with which are then destroyed those men whose brains are of less capacity. In such a world Neanderthal Man disappears, Homo sapiens flourishes. The brains of men become rapidly more capable of thought.

In a world of fixed forms we fix on the form we know best, our own. In search of significant story we refer back to Creation when all forms began. Religion is a drama between God and man. All else is stage. All history is the history of man.

In a world of evolution partitions vanish, forms merge, disappear, transform themselves cloudlike. We flee then this ruin of forms, cling to that larger form, life. In search of significant story we refer back to that imagined moment, the advent of life, when began the long march of developing forms. History is the chronicle of evolution. Religion seeks the sacredness of life.

In a world of spirit, life itself dissolves. That imagined first animate particle, that huge, hungry, and suddenly self-replicating molecule—a hero of sorts to be sure, but not so radically different from, nor discontinuous with, that tangle of protein and nucleic acid, only a bit more sluggish, that preceded it—had itself been elaborated of simpler constituents in continuous creation over millions of years into unfathomable complexity. Miracle is not once but everywhere and all the time. Something there is that is larger than life, intangible, abstract, including life but including more, including all. In search of significant story we refer back to the beginning of all; for all things have become one. Religion goes in search of spirit, is itself spirit. Spirit finds a mirror in man, sees itself.

As guiding light for this journey without end, the shift of referent from life to spirit is a move to unity. For the concept of the sacredness of life is forever vulnerable to those who agree, and who then add that some lives are more sacred than others, some forms of life more precious than other forms. But we shall not ask *which* spirit, there is but one, nor *whose* spirit, for it belongs to no one, not even to life itself. We are but the bearers.

Descartes promised we would become lords and possessors of the universe, and so we have—and are well on our way to destroy it. Out of the window flies reverence. Why must we forever look up to the man with the sword, down on the man who kneels? As lords and possessors we seize and usurp, proceed triumphantly to bleak destruction. As bearers we might find something to worship, might honor our burden, recover reverence.

III

GRAIL-HUNGER

THE advertisement of the travel agency shows a black-haired girl in the surf at Acapulco: black bikini, shoulders hunched forward exposing the heft of breasts. She is laughing hysterically, her long hair hanging wet, one hand raised to the side of her face in a gesture of vulnerability, a movement that bespeaks the capacity for passion and tenderness. I study the picture with an intentness both savage and desolate. Desire springs up, envelops her, pushes beyond the presenting laughter, beyond the innocent beach games, into the hotel behind her, takes her into the privacy of a luxurious room where an incandescent erotism, the heart and soul of this vacation, is to occur. Is this the way the ad-man wants me to think? It works! It works!

In the hospital a nurse walks toward me down a long hallway: tight white uniform pulled into slight transverse wrinkles across the full hips (I slow my pace), white stockings, full round face, Italian romantic style, broad soft mouth, very dark eyes and eye-brows (I stop), white skin, glistening black hair, straight and soft, drawn back loosely across her ears (I'm backing up a bit now). Just before she passes, the liquid eyes look up, and for a moment the face is transformed with a smile of breath-catching trustful-ness.

Longing mounts, becomes frantic. If I had one I'd want the other. I want both, I want them all. I ascribe to these creatures a quality of heaven, a gift of re-demption, a love that would enable me to become what I am not, will never be.

One afternoon I go into the secretarial office to get a chart from the files, and in so doing brush against Sonya. She nods and we pass. A moment later we bump again; for we are reaching into the same drawer and, as it turns out, for the same chart. We smile, she offers it to me, I defer to her, and the incident is over. But in that moment I have noticed her eyes—eloquent, tragic, remote—and something has begun. During the next few days I notice many other things about her, and what is happening to me, I see, is happening also to her. It progresses quickly: sitting together, holding hands, the sharing of se-crets, embracing, and two weeks after the encounter at the filing cabinet we are in a motel outside Hart-ford, deeply in love, wondering what to do.

Life becomes a strange mixture of the mean and the tender, of clandestine meetings, lying to wife, dissimulating before colleagues, fabricating excuses, furtive weekends. We are in each other's offices almost constantly, sneaking in and out in the hope of avoiding notice. Occasionally we lie together on my office couch, fearful that someone may knock, and I feel a strange unease at the thought that presently I will be sitting *behind* this couch, considering with clinical detachment, presumably, just such prisons of passion as this. Sonya is an apostle of intimacy, her joy the breaching of barriers. We find in each other such intensity, such deepening fulfillment, that the relationship becomes the greatest possible good. I stop seeking how to live, I *know.* For the first time work becomes the ordinary activity of a happy man rather than a driven and tormented struggle. Guiltily we begin to consider divorce and remarriage.

After a few months things become difficult. Our colleagues begin to sense something. Rumor of our affair spreads among the patients. We begin to have fights. Sonya weeps and clings to me as if we were being torn apart, says we must end it because of my children. I decide to proceed with a divorce, she dissuades me. A sane decision is not possible in this setting, the strain is too great. We have to get away somehow, be with each other alone and in peace. I fabricate a research conference in New Orleans, and

Sonya is reportedly called to Europe on business. Leaving separately, we meet the following day in New York and take a plane for Mexico.

We have then our time of being with each other alone. For a month we travel together without meeting anyone we know. Yet things go wrong from the start. Nothing sudden, nothing definite; we have no fights, but something is awry. We are puzzled and anxious.

I don't know why it has happened but after a few days I know what has happened: the magic is gone. She had been the woman without whom I could not live; now she is only a woman very dear to me. We had for each other an affinity which flowered into love. This we have lost and do not find again. When I ask myself if I love her I feel sure I do, but I never had to ask before. It is a sensible love now, capable of being weighed in the same balance with contending claims.

I can tell she feels as I, but we are ashamed and do not talk about it. She says our trouble is that we are running away, which makes us feel like cowards. Another time she says she feels guilty toward her husband and I, toward my wife and children. I agree, but it isn't my wife toward whom I feel guilty, but Sonya. I am sad and bewildered by our loss but not deeply upset, nostalgic but not determined to have it back, and feel guilty because of not being more distressed.

We seem willing to let it be lost, make only token efforts to find it again.

In the afternoon we sit in the village square in Taxco before the crumbling cathedral. Children swarm around us offering fake antiquities. At dusk we walk up the narrow cobblestone path to the hotel at the top of the hill. The lonely Englishman, drinking gin as always in the damp lobby, looks up with a sickly smile in the hope we will stop to chat with him. In our room we close the door, and standing there by the cold bed embrace tenderly and are enveloped by such a stillness the world seems deserted. Our relationship has become sentimental; we treat each other with unusual gentleness. In Oaxaca we walk behind the loquacious guide through the ruined streets of Monte Alban and Mitla, holding hands, saying little, feeling a deep affection, knowing the madness is gone. Our exaltation had been the meaning of life; and the sad thing is that, having lost it, we are willing to deem it madness. We love each other but are no longer *in* love, are good for each other but no longer indispensable. It does not seem justified to break up two marriages in order to make a third which would be no more final than either of those we would be scrapping. We do not talk about it, the decision is implicit. When our month is up and we start back we know what has been decided.

We created for each other an illusion. We fell in

love, not with each other, but each with the image of himself in the other's eyes. These reflections, flashing back and forth, expanded a modest affection into an overwhelming passion. At the file cabinet I saw a tragic beauty in her face, and on that foundation built a fairy castle. For at that moment she saw my perception of her, found the image pleasing, and thought better of me for my discernment. My next perception discovered in her, therefore, not only the beauty already noticed, but her enhanced appraisal of me; whereupon I realized her to be a woman of unusual sensitivity. And when next she glanced at me she noticed this added element in my perception of her, which led her again to revise upward her image of me. So it progressed, with lightning rapidity. I came to believe that she had found in me something for which she would risk all she had, and I responded with thumping affirmation of that fineness in her which enabled her to discover this quality in me. But she had looked, not into my heart, but into the mirror of my eyes and had seen there an embellished image of herself. A single candle of affection, reflected back and forth between us, became a blaze of illumination and, finally, the meaning of life itself.

Such a passion feeds on its own hunger, consumes itself. We could not long live on reflected appraisals. There are other things to life, troubles and tasks and preoccupations, and one day, looking at Sonya, I see, not myself, but her concern with other persons, other matters. Failing to find in her that retouched portrait of myself to which I have become so attached, I no longer feel that passionate approval of her which she had so merited. And when next she looks at me she fails to see herself, for I too have other concerns, or else finds an image of herself scaled down from that to which she has become accustomed, whereupon her feeling for me is correspondingly diminished.

It was a small thing that got this magic started, and a small thing that made it start to disappear. Of all those qualities which I perceived in her when I was so enraptured, only one is now missing. Everything else is still there—the soft hair, the receptive body, the generous heart, the impassioned spirit—but the blaze of love has diminished to the candlelight of affection and left us where we started. The affair has ended, but we remain friends. I think of her fondly; and sometimes, looking at her across the conference table, I feel her in my arms again, hear her whispering that she cannot live without me. She has developed the habit of chewing slightly at the inside of her cheek, which gives her face a ruminative cast. For a while after our return from Mexico she was remote and sad, but now her old intensity and enthusiasm have returned.

Apostate without alternative creed, I'm sick in search of something holy. Grail-hunger is making me mad.

To kneel in fear is despicable. In our stricken nights we struggle to hold honor above survival. Evil lurks and we stride forever the silent streets of fear.

Not to kneel at all is madness, is to look only down, to be alone in the universe, to have no place in anything larger than one's self.

To kneel in reverence, by choice, without fear, this is man's glory.

Ah but where is God? Where might we find him?

What we find when we search upward we call God. Aspiration lays hold, draws us up. We revere, we kneel. But gods grow old and die, fall foolish, become tyrants—whereupon kneeling man must stand and destroy them.

Sometimes we surprise our gods, come upon them in their dressing rooms. Dolls in disarray, tinted as flesh but clay of hand and foot and visage. We were the sculptor. They are of our making, not greater than ourselves, but of ourselves. We then become God, stand at the summit, look only down. To gods nothing is holy. We lose our limits, go mad.

When all the gods are gone, when we look up and find nothing, when the ground on which we stand has become the pinnacle of the universe, then we

must send up a beacon. And when it finds no pur-
chase in that murk, illumines no face, then it is that
pillar of light itself, straining upward, fraying out in
blackness, greater than ourselves, that is God.

Girls! They have but to walk by to suck out of me
longing as a whirlwind takes up straw. In this land,
however rich I become, whatever castles I acquire,
so long as I possess not these girls I shall be a starve-
ling with a dry mouth.

Sex is the only experiencing which could justify
living, draw me back from an abstract future to a
present of palpable skin. I loiter at the newsstand.
Lust creeps over me. Fingers itch. Not even the
humiliation of having to put on my glasses stays my
hand from the centerfolds. The old images ride up
into consciousness, ravage and usurp. They show me
what I want but do not go beyond the encounter.

The encounter would, however, have consequences, and what would be the fate of lust among
those consequences? What way would life tend? Pur-
suit, capture, penetration, explosion—what then?
The current is suddenly off, the magnet exerts no
pull, the white flesh under my hand is not magic, is
just a woman. But isn't that a crash, to have felt for
her such a yearning, to have attained her, to be lying
now in her arms, yet have no desire, no need, no
cherishing, nothing to bind her to me or me to her?

What is to follow? Getting up? dressing? parting? Could I tolerate a life of such encounters, of relationships so truncated? Would I not rather be appalled that the exalted and selfless relatedness of which man is capable can be reduced to this carnal straining at each other? Would I not be moved to elevate it, to transform it into love? And would not that loving, because of its more intimate connections with dependence and vulnerability, come quickly to place faithfulness above variety? And would not then the mind and character of one's lover, her style, generosity, and above all her heart—qualities all more rare and special, and much harder to find, than physical contours—would not these things stand forth as what I sought, displacing the curves of undifferentiated flesh which plague me now? And would not this vision of what, in those circumstances, I would most desperately want, be, indeed, exactly what I already have?

Whence then this ache for which, even in principle, there is no relief? this hunger that can be fed but never satisfied?

Girl-hunger, grail-hunger—two views, perhaps, of the same striving. Lips and legs, smiles and breasts, drawing us on, ceaselessly—is this not spirit thrusting itself into the future, creating and extending itself into ever more knowing forms of life, rushing on profligately, endlessly, through wave after wave of unresisting and expendable flesh? It sweeps through us, uses us, discards us, whirls on into a future we shall not know. Yet we yearn terribly, not to be left behind. We want to be, not the medium through which the wave passes, but the wave itself which rushes on. So we go searching after God—and is this not spirit, becoming aware of itself, reaching for a vision of that toward which it moves? We want to see what it is this striving strives toward. Being used, we seek to know the purpose we serve, want then to give to the great design our holiest word, God.

On being asked "Do you love each other?" those who live only in the present become confused, do not understand the question, don't know what to say. "We get along," they say uneasily, or "We get a lot of kicks," or "We get it together."

Love is created anew by each generation from lust and loneliness. For this to come about, primary needs may not be primarily spent, must be accumulated. But the promiscuous accumulate nothing. They wander about improvidently paying out the common need in a common and recurrent coupling, never bringing together enough of the elemental drives, never subjecting them to sufficient pressure, to ignite them into love.

What eventually becomes reality appears first as illusion. The hope attached to illusion sustains life when all else is lost.

ON NOT KNOWING HOW TO LIVE

All my life I have been in search of God. That's why I've never been able to enjoy anything. One has to have found God—to have a place in something larger than one's self, to which one belongs—to enjoy anything. Lacking it one is in anguished search, or else, despairing, becomes one's self God and then is responsible for everything.

A woman of lively interests is my wife. She loves to travel, to walk about in strange cities, breathe a foreign air, hear another tongue. Swimming delights her; the presumptuous intimacy of the unresisting medium makes her laugh. She likes to talk with friends, always wants to know what they are doing, to hear about their children. She loves to walk, to feel the sun on her face, to browse in new stores, to visit museums and look reverently upon the past.

All these things, so desirable to her, I find tedious. She does not, however, like to do them alone; so I go along and, while apparently participating, actually am waiting for whatever it is we are doing to be done with. And as I go on like this, tolerating in benign martyrdom a way of life created from her initiative, it comes somehow to seem that, on my own, I could arrange things better, that I *know* how to live, but am constrained by her needs to banal diversions.

One day something goes wrong with my knee. I'm not so crippled as I portray, but enough to be excused from obligations. My wife is all sympathy, tells me it will get better. "What do you want to do?" she says. "Come! Get in the car. I'll drive. It's a marvelous day. We'll go anywhere you want, do anything you like. It's Sunday, it's springtime, the sun is shining. You mustn't be sad. Where do you want to go?"

I have no idea. Anywhere. Nowhere. My mind is, not blank, but neutral. Places parade before imagination and all are equal. She drives us to the beach, thousands of people swimming, oiling themselves on bright towels, playing in the sand; along a golf course where we pause to watch a man take three practice swings, then hit a perfect drive, the ball sailing straight away, up, up, and out of sight; by a museum with a show of French Impressionists, throngs of people entering and leaving. In the park we drive by picnickers, teen-agers throwing Frisbees, barefoot girls playing volleyball, young couples pushing baby carriages, smells of cooking, of charcoal fires, sounds of baseball, of guitars, and of laughter. My wife, delighted with this panorama, drives slowly, glances at me eagerly, ready to stop wherever my inclination may suggest, do anything I want, go on to any place I wish, while I, looking out on this unhesitating life process, fall into a well.

Every one of these people *knows* what to do, how to enjoy it. It looks terribly simple, yet I have not the knack. I can *do* these things, go through the motions, simulate the responses—to an observer it might seem that I, too, know how to enjoy a holiday—but in the manner of a brain-damaged patient who, thinking intently what each leg must do, can somehow get there, but not with a natural walk. I lack a kind of native knowing which is the legacy of everything that lives. Now, suddenly, without the obligation to do those many things which, as it seemed, I have not really wanted to do, I have nothing better to put in their place, indeed nothing whatever to put in their place. Free, I cannot improvise. Relieved of my burden, I am bereft.

How strange! I have worked hard all week, now along comes a day of utter leisure. Must there not be something I want? something that would give me pleasure? I must observe these people more closely. There must be a secret, some simple solution.

Always and forever the student and still I don't know how. Are there no classes in living? Would someone take me as an apprentice?

Not knowing how to live is separateness, the division of the world into self and others. I sit inside my skull and look out as a frightened man from a moated castle. Me in here and the world out there. We negotiate, we make deals, exchanges, but we are not one. I am an entity, complete. Never do I lose sight of where I stop and the world begins. With sleepless vigilance I patrol the edges of selfhood, warn visitors away. I am independent within this domain, but am dying. It is my wholeness that destroys me. I long for partness in a greater whole.

Knowing how to live is oneness with the world. I die of the hunger of oneness. I find it never. I read about it, and the words are ghosts. Dharma is not for me, nor "the way" of Lao Tzu. I feel it in the patience of trees, the wind in their branches sighs about it. I hear it in the rote of the surf and the song of the lark. I see it in animals and in children. I touch it but cannot make it mine. *Mine!* I'm trying to grab it, I suppose, ravage it back into this moated castle, and that's the trouble—this division of everything into self and others which I can't escape because it's not something that limits me, it *is* me.

Our remote ancestor floating in a warm sea was in intimate contact and exchange with that sea through the film which formed its boundary, vulnerable to every change. In cold water life subsided, over salt flats it ended. Death was by misadventure, but misadventure was everywhere and always; for there was no change, however slight, in the sustaining fluid against which the organism was protected.

But in time one cell becomes many, becomes a creature, differentiates into parts, folds in upon itself, captures a bit of that warm ocean, encloses it forever.

Outer cells harden while inner cells, shielded now from contingency, live in an inland sea the composition of which is held constant. An unpredictable environment has been internalized and dominated. The boundary line of life becomes less permeable. Suspicious and contractile orifices appear to handle necessary interchange. Membrane becomes skin, fin, shell, becomes clothes, armor, castle, moat, Maginot Line.

I feel a desperate uncertainty and misery, want and know not what I want, seek and know that nothing ever will satisfy this seeking—no fame, no love, nothing. I stand on a ledge.

We are held in life by commitments, as broken bone by a plaster cast. "The man who desisted from committing suicide because he heard the factory whistle blow," writes C. E. Ayres, "was thereby recognizing a profound truth, namely, that his existence is so intertwined with those of other people that his death must inevitably send forth waves of disturbance and interruption, affecting most those who are closest to him but also prejudicing, to however tiny an extent, the whole effort of mankind."

I have severed relations with the factory, the whistle blows but not for me. I cling to non-attachment even as I suffer from it. For so long has it been my way that, however wrong in principle, it has become for me right. I owe it loyalty. It has come to be the source of all that I can do. Desperate unrest is my workshop.

"None but the truths which have been extracted under mental torture appeal to us," writes Cyril Connolly.

To turn from spirit is to deny life, for life is part of spirit. There is nothing to worship but that great wind which animates the universe, hurricaning the corridors of time, catching up matter, hurling it into form, achieving life, consciousness, civilization, the spires of Chartres, the prayers of Rilke, the cry of Mahler, the indomitability of Beethoven. To worship spirit, to look back over its long course, affirm it, identify ourselves with it, renouncing all there is in us at variance, committing all the rest to spirit's cause, adding to its reach and thrust that little push which is our life, claiming thereby spirit's grandeur, knowing that at this moment it moves forward only in us, that were we to fall it too would fall—so to serve is man's honor, glory, his greatest good, his true worship.

IV

THE TASK

NOTHING endures but a futile yearning. There's a natural grace to youth, age hovers on the grotesque.

I'll try no more to force myself into acts of creation on a field of nihilism. I must find new ground. What I seek is a vision of life within which love and joy are possible. I cannot go back to discarded beliefs of the past, cannot go on in this desert, must seek something new.

Seek to find or seek to create?

We are plunging down a cataract, and what's important is to call out. Not for help, there is no help. Not in despair—what can anyone do but shrug, look away? But to give a signal. A gesture of love and humor to acknowledge drowning so others who drown will know they are not alone. We are all drowning; deny it with blindness, transcend it with laughter. The laughter I seek is that which looks straight in the eye of despair and laughs. The proper subjects for comedy are fear, loneliness, and death.

I dream of escape, a change of view, a different life, a rebirth perhaps of the will to go on searching. One more surge, Lord, before I'm through.

Life as the acting out of illusion, life as the achievement of meaning. The distinction itself may be illusory. Maybe there is no meaning but only life; and in art, no meaning but only the illusion of life. Maybe that's the whole thing—to observe life so closely, to search it out so carefully, with so much love, that it comes alive, that it *is*.

A holiday in summer. I go in the afternoon in bright sunshine to sit in a dark and nearly empty theater. As I wait for the film to begin, the sour loneliness of the place settles on my spirit. Yesterday's cigarette smoke in the air, balls of hardened gum under the armrests, popcorn and candy wrappers on the floor. I and a few other bleak souls wait dumbly like oxen in the rain for deliverance, each of us isolated in the drizzle of his own everyday misery.

The house darkens, the music begins, the screen is illuminated, deliverance is at hand. *The Bicycle Thief.* The few of us sitting there, dispersed, walled off from each other by pain and distrust, by a kind of stubborn uncaring, become a community as we watch. We are shown a poor man trying to find work. We see his wife, his son, we feel their fear, the loom of hunger. Gradually de Sica's love of this man makes him come alive, makes him human. The thief who steals his bicycle is faceless, beyond notice, one of the ignominious and detestable of the earth. All our sympathy goes to his victim who, without the bicycle, will lose his job. We follow him in his desperate search, feel with him, suffer his frustration, enter his despair, finally *become* him—then *he* steals a bicycle! And, suddenly, *we* have stolen a bicycle, are one with all men, high and low, good and bad, and weep for all that is faceless and voiceless and moves with heavy heart over the dark earth.

What a grand thing de Sica does, what a great and disinterested love to take as its object this limited, thwarted, and weak man, and, by going out to him with such caring, such patient observing, to make him not only live—though that's miracle enough— but our brother! I most deeply salute a man with the soul to do that. And if ever I find myself seeking out the privileged, the interesting, the beautiful, I hope I will remember the bicycle thief and that I am he.

Exaltation leaps up in us from an image, a song, a phrase. And since these things conjure the feeling, the value of the feeling attaches to the thing which gives it birth; and the making of these things becomes our greatest good, the best we can do.

So fragile the relation of symbol to exaltation, so exhaustible the magic! The noblest music palls. But then other music will invoke the spell. So the creation must go on forever, endless weaving of new nets to capture again and again that deep joyousness which leads to further enlargement of spirit.

The objective mode is not for me, the detached voice rings false. I must work from the formlessness of my own life, speak in my own voice, however faltering and unsure. What I seek is not to be found in my past, is not to be found at all but achieved, but must be achieved, if at all, from the debris and clutter of a flawed and limping life. I admonish myself: Give up this longing for a past of brave adventure from which to work. Heroic experience is hearsay, is not your own. Don't just stand there in lamentation before the junk-heap of memory, the fears and evasions, the missed opportunities, the cautious advances. Wade in. Pick up the pieces. Don't expect to *find* anything of value. This is ore, not metal. Expect only to come upon something—slingshot, love letter, rusted foil, ancient condom, broken knight from a chess set—from which with effort and courage something of beauty might be made.

The writing of books imposes on nameless need a rhythm, a cycle, one book every three or four years and then repeat. First emptiness, wandering around within myself in a void. All is dark, and darkness thickens; hands before my face touch things vanishing and unrecognizable. Void becomes chaos. I stumble, seek, encounter slime, terrifying shapes. I become frantic, I despair. I flee outside myself, escape into distractions, chess, tennis. (Tennis! Forcing old bones into the big game, straining up into the sun for the serve, lumbering to the net, taking the volley at my unwilling feet, then back for the lob, trying to forget the absurdity of these movements as seen through a doorway which blocks out one of the players.) But I cannot rest with tennis—or with chess or drinking or collecting things. Distractions contend with a call; I am accountable to a mysterious tribunal which convenes at night in the darkness within, and despair is but a breath away, and I'll never write another book, the last one is the last ever. I am nevertheless summoned and must live with this chaos till a pattern appears.

Then somehow, never to be explained, there comes a vision. No, rather the ghost of a vision. Something seizes, and illumines, a region of murk, intimates form, points a way. Exhilaration then and the beginning of work, the shaping of vision. First draft, second draft, delete, discard, revise, final draft; the polishing of sentences, the reading aloud for qualities of sound, for rhythm, assonance. At last it's ready, I let it go. To the agony and grandeur of spirit I have borne witness. I feel a kind of triumph, a radiance.

And does such testimony make a difference? Don't hold your breath. Silence, silence, silence. A feather has fallen into an abyss. Months pass and finally a few echoes are heard. Friends applaud, strangers write. People read and are moved. The book stays in print, means something, must be thought a success. Yet I feel, not fulfillment, but an obscure spreading disappointment, a bearable private hurt, some withdrawal, a sense that somehow this misses, is not what I intended, that this isn't it.

In World War II—that honorable war in which even jokes about evading service had a quality of innocence—the medics told of a soldier who would drop his rifle on the battlefield and run to pick up any little scrap of paper, would examine it eagerly, then sorrowfully shake his head as the paper fluttered to the ground. Hospitalized, he remained mute, his compulsion obscure and intractable. He wandered forlornly about the psychiatric ward picking up scraps of paper, each time with discernible hope followed by inevitable dejection. Pronounced unfit for service, he received one day his discharge from the army, whereupon he found his voice. "This is it!" he cried. "This is it!"

I am that soldier but without that happy ending. Nothing is it, and nothing, ever, will be it. Fame, universal acclaim, being loved by everyone? Dizzying to consider, but I have grown wise and know that even that would not be it. I, too, will get my discharge one day, but that won't be it either. I will go quietly.

Now it is the time, if ever, to utter a sound, to give a signal.

I do not use myself up in living. A part of myself I save, like a miser, hoping to transmute it into something that will go on living for me in the future. With the quick I have little to do; the eminent dead are my models, the yet unborn my legatees. I am a time-binder, obsessed with mortality, spend my life creating an effigy to outlast me. In the graveyard, ceaselessly I carve at my epitaph, trying to make of it something so beautiful, so compact of meaning, that people will come from afar to read.

It need not be in vain, this elaboration of self—great treasures have been so fashioned. What gets served up to the future may be a tasty dish indeed, but what shall we say of the chef, oblivious of the hungry ones around him, garnishing himself for the gourmets of the future? Rather than miss a day of painting, Cézanne did not attend his mother's funeral. Rilke could not spare from his poetry the time for his daughter's wedding. The world cannot do without such people, but pity those whose lot it is to live with them.

I think rather more of those who use themselves up, die with nothing left over, disappear without a trace. My wife holds nothing back, spends her life on the living, gives herself to the hungry who feed on her, consume her substance. I see her getting smaller, becoming transparent, beginning to disappear. But look at her face! It grows finer, more beautiful! She has time. Come and be fed. She prepares no delicacies for the future, but soup today for everyone, even for those hungry chefs who think only of future banquets. Better get to know her now, for she will soon be gone, and you'll not then recover her from the history of our time. But without the likes of her there would be no future for which the present could be a history.

I find myself wanting to fall in love again. With her of the volatile spirit, the open and generous heart. I have been holding myself aloof for years, invulnerable, to protect the search. But love can't live on the shelf, must be fed with those confidences which create vulnerability. Without risk of hurt there is no love. Not, anyway, of the kind we used to have, she and I—the soaring, the despair, the exaltation. Now I have no search to protect, have lost direction, find nothing, create nothing, want back the deep, deep joy. I must open myself to pain, must see it as minor beside the passion it makes possible.

I have defined and clarified the nihilistic position until it includes everything, and goodness itself becomes a random throw. Yet even so it is unthinkable not to try. Standing by the freeway and seeing there before me in the fast lane an injured child, would I not try?

But there *is* an injured child. In Vietnam, Biafra, Bangladesh, Babi Yar—the list is endless. Always there is an injured child. Of what trying then am I capable, I who for so long have burrowed within, ever more deeply down and inward, who live now in an airless world of phantoms, who no longer know even where the fast lane is?

I must give up this lamentation. Life offers no task with transcendent authorization, no goal the accomplishment of which can be guaranteed to have lasting value. I must accept that whatever I undertake is as risky, of both achievement and value, as darting out on that freeway. Probably I shall be killed before reaching the child, or, if I succeed in snatching him up, he will die of injuries already received—or survive to become a murderer. There's nothing sure to go on—only that it's unthinkable not to try, that there isn't anything else. If ultimate tasks are illusory I must have at the tasks near at hand, at the transient tasks, the cries for help in a confused and changing field.

I fall at times into such a brave, constructive mood. It doesn't last. The possibility of doing useful work commands no energies of mine. What these energies will respond to, and to nothing else, is a task which is faithful to the crushing and exceptionless nihilism by which I am riven and yet shot through—like Mahler's Ninth Symphony—with a vision of lyric beauty. The former without the latter is intolerable; the latter without the former is trivial. I must maintain the search for a task which will embody both. Were I to find it, energies would become available, would bend to this vision.

V

THE PATH
OF SPIRIT

"MAN is the vessel of the Spirit," writes Erich Heller; ". . . Spirit is the voyager who, passing through the land of man, bids the human soul to follow it to the Spirit's purely spiritual destination."

Viewed closely, the path of spirit is seen to meander, is a glisten of snail's way in night forest; but from a height minor turnings merge into steadiness of course. Man has reached a ledge from which to look back. For thousands of years the view is clear, and beyond, though a haze, for thousands more, we still see quite a bit. The horizon is millions of years behind us. Beyond the vagrant turnings of our last march stretches a shining path across that vast expanse running straight. Man did not begin it nor will he end it, but makes it now, finds the passes, cuts the channels. Whose way is it we so further? Not man's; for there's our first footprint. Not life's; for there's still the path when life was not yet.

59

Spirit is the traveler, passes now through the realm of man. We did not create spirit, do not possess it, cannot define it, are but the bearers. We take it up from unmourned and forgotten forms, carry it through our span, will pass it on, enlarged or diminished, to those who follow. Spirit is the voyager, man is the vessel.

Spirit creates and spirit destroys. Creation without destruction is not possible; destruction without creation feeds on past creation, reduces form to matter, tends toward stillness. Spirit creates more than it destroys (though not in every season, nor even every age, hence those meanderings, those turnings back, wherein the longing of matter for stillness triumphs in destruction) and this preponderance of creation makes for that over-all steadiness of course.

From primal mist of matter to spiraled galaxies and clockwork solar systems, from molten rock to an earth of air and land and water, from heaviness to lightness to life, sensation to perception, memory to consciousness—man now holds a mirror, spirit sees itself. Within the river currents turn back, eddies whirl. The river itself falters, disappears, emerges, moves on. The general course is the growth of form, increasing awareness, matter to mind to consciousness. The harmony of man and nature is to be found in continuing this journey along its ancient course toward greater freedom and awareness.

If one accepts Christianity as true and takes it seriously one becomes a flagellant or a Knight Templar. The flagellant is overwhelmed by the sin within himself, the lust, envy, greed, vanity, is crushed by a guilt he knows to be irremediable; for even though he be absolved it will be but minutes before he sins again. So it is with saints and martyrs, so it was with those monks of the Pechevsky Monastery who lived out their lives in the eternal darkness of tiny cells deep in the catacombs, and so it has been with thousands of simple men who over the centuries suffered and died lifting the heavy stone of the earth up into gothic spires.

The Knight Templar, more free perhaps in aggression, disposed to dominate rather than to submit, turns away from the sin within and identifies himself with the authority which condemns this sin. It takes two, he observes, to create the dialogue of man and God, and he leaps easily from the cringing sinner to the condemning judge, becomes a priest, a knight of the Crusades, a soldier of the Inquisition, a hammer of God to beat down the spirit of sinful man.

The religion of my childhood was dominated by guilt. Sin was continuous, absolution but momentary, and guilt the daily lot. I became a flagellant without recompense—no redemption, no ecstacy, no union with God. Never was I lifted to exaltation or joy, never was I granted some enlargement of spirit, but was beaten down, crushed in unworthiness, crumpled up in God's hand and tossed aside.

From such humiliation an upright position is recovered, usually, by covert disbelief. One no longer takes religion seriously, treats it rather as an ailing and querulous aunt, with outward respect but not really listening, a leftover from the past, no longer of any importance, and anyway soon to be dead. Religion thereupon becomes ritualized hypocrisy, and the religious experience is lost. Spirituality is discredited because religion, officially the guardian of spirit, is falsely professed and falsely maintained. Such is the way of most people of the Western world in the Modern Age. It leads to a progressively secular society which yet maintains a mask of piety. The spiritual life is impoverished.

There is another way up from one's knees: one may rebel, may shake one's fist at God. Such was the way I found. As soon as it became known to me that the biblical story is incompatible with the known history of life on earth I enlisted intellect in an attack on Christianity—on ritual, dogma, promise, miracle, salvation. I pushed this attack very far, did not stop until the citadel was, for me, in ruins; for, having escaped, I was intent never again to be caught. I would live as a free spirit in a secular world, would know this world by the unaided effort of reason, would trust reason alone.

But anguish lurks at every corner, and reason is slow, is a cold comfort. One turns naturally to God or, if God is dead, to something else greater than man, and therein lies the danger of a new bondage, to that "something greater than man." The tendency is insidious, judgment may be destroyed before one knows it has been impaired. Vigilance is not enough, the danger must be excluded in principle. To make sure that, even in direst need, I would never trade freedom for solace I asserted that there does not *exist* anything above the mind of man, that there is nothing in the universe with which reason cannot cope. I marched with inflexible resolution and militancy into a world of the matter-of-fact. Adventure and challenge were increased, mystery and wonder were diminished, reverence was lost. I had escaped guilt by agreeing to a constriction of spirit.

My life copies like a child's first tracing the history of the Western world. I know not of a Golden Age, but my mother adored me and I easily imagine an age of bliss at her breast. Likewise lost is my classical period, those few years following infancy when I could hurl myself upon the world without loss of innocence, when aggression was natural, when action came easily. I can but surmise there must have been such a time, brief, beyond memory. What I do remember is the beginning of my Middle Ages when I was seized in the grip of conscience. This time of guilt, of bondage to God, which for the West lasted ten centuries, for me lasted ten years. My discovery in adolescence that the Christian story conflicts with fact, that God's account, therefore, is not to be trusted but must be skeptically examined and checked, reenacts the beginning of the Modern Age when Copernicus found, against the revelation of Holy Writ, that the earth revolves about the sun, when Galileo began to insist that observed truth must take precedence over revealed truth. "Methinks that in the discussion of natural problems," Galileo wrote, "we ought not to begin at the authority of places of Scripture, but at sensible experiments and necessary illustration. . . . Nature, being inexorable and immutable, and never passing the bounds of the laws assigned her . . . I conceive that, concerning natural effects, that which either sensible experience sets before our eyes, or necessary demonstrations do prove unto us, ought not, on any account, be called into question, much less condemned upon the testimony of texts of Scripture, which may, under their words, couch senses seemingly contrary thereto." My determination to know the world by the unaided effort of reason copies Bacon and Descartes. "I perceived it to be possible," wrote Descartes, "to arrive at knowledge highly useful in life, and instead of the speculative philosophy usually taught in the schools, to discover a practical [method] by means of which, knowing the force and action of fire, water, air, the stars, the heavens, and all the other bodies that surround us, as distinctly as we know the various crafts of our artisans, we might also apply them in the same way to all the uses to which they are adapted, and thus render ourselves the lords and possessors of nature." My efforts in science strain after the spectacular scientific achievements of the Modern Age. The constriction of spirit which these efforts have entailed mirrors the wasteland of spirit at which the West has arrived.

In adolescence my quarrel with God was private; I did not seek to discredit him with others, sought only to escape his bondage. So it was, also, with those philosophers who brought into being the Modern Age. They made no campaign to destroy the Church, struggled but to free themselves of its restrictions; did not seek followers for a new faith, resolved only to be independent of any irrational authority. They knew that there is in man an abiding spiritual hunger to which the Church, albeit with decreasing efficacy, still ministered, and that if they should attempt to destroy the Church, having no new one with which to replace it, they would fail as well as offend. In saying that religion is the opiate of the masses Marx but expresses what all the shapers of the modern world have believed—that the need for religion is a measure of intellectual weakness and that this weakness will be overcome eventually by enlightenment.

In the meantime the intellectual and scientific leaders, leaving to the masses their holy opiate, will push on to see what can be accomplished by the unaided mind of man, confident that the ensuing achievements will be so spectacular (as, indeed, they have turned out to be) that the rest of mankind will follow along with increasing confidence and decreasing fear until the need for religion will have disappeared and we all shall live comfortably and happily in the godless world of the future.

The conflict between science and spirit is critical, possibly even fatal; for it could lead to the disappearance from the earth of all that spirit has achieved during the time of man. Yet this conflict is not necessary, not entailed by opposing principles; for the relation of science to spirit is of part to whole. During the Modern Age science has been the leading edge of spirit. There was a time perhaps, long ago, when the forward movement of spirit was carried by religion; but during the last five hundred years it has been that cast of mind that puts its faith in reason and calls for tangible proof by which spirit has advanced. And the gains of spirit during this period exceed all achievements of the past, being inclusive of more space and time, more greatly extending vision, ever further emancipating spirit from matter.

The conflict between science and spirit derives

from the tendency of science to assume it is the whole of spirit rather than spirit's currently most useful medium. This tendency proceeds mainly by way of the disparagement by science of all those movements and expressions of spirit which cannot readily be assimilated to or explained by scientific method. What cannot be known by critical rationalism, science likes to assume, cannot be known at all, and what cannot be known does not exist. Scientific method yields truth because it yields control; control, therefore, becomes the means whereby to test truth, becomes insidiously the criterion of truth. All other ways by which man reaches out to know the world are assumed to yield but ignorance, confusion, superstition. Science so claims the whole of truth, and what value can there be in what remains? The ranges of spirit beyond science become vague, illusory.

Looking back over the evolutionary spectacle of cumulative form-building, most of which took place before the advent of man and hence, certainly, before science—clouds of hydrogen collapsing to form helium, molecules arranging themselves into crystals, life arising from matter—science does not see an evolving spirit which in billions of years will eventually flower into science itself, sees only causal processes occurring in matter and, later, in animate beings, but without purpose or meaning. Science, coming into existence only in the latest moment of a universal and timeless process, claims to stand apart from that process, to be possessed of a qualitative difference, asserts that it alone can understand the process, discover the inexorable laws which govern it and which do not themselves change but simply are the way things are. By this attitude science, though itself one of the grandest expressions of spirit, disparages all of spirit which is not science.

The aim of life is to multiply. Every amoeba wants to become two amoebae. Rabbits would transform the food supply of the world into rabbits, rats would transform it into rats. No sense of moderation leads them to desist; they are halted by other forms of life bent on their own designs of transformation. The food supply of the world, for any species, is everything else that lives. Success in the struggle for reproduction is at the expense of other living forms driven by the same motivation.

In this context occur those random accidents in the genetic code which are thereafter translated, faithfully and in perpetuity, into altered structure and function. When such alteration hinders in the struggle to reproduce, the bearers of the alteration disappear; when it facilitates, the bearers become more numerous. "Evolution is built on accidents," writes François Jacob, "on chance events, on errors. The very thing that would lead an inert system to destruction becomes a source of novelty and complexity in a living system. An accident can be transformed into an innovation, an error into success. For natural selection is a game with its own rules. All that counts are the changes that affect the number of offspring. If they reduce that number, they are mistakes; if they increase it, they are exploits. There are neither tricks nor stratagems in the game; only a careful score of profit and loss. Reproduction directs the course of chance."

A favorable variation for one species may be fatal for its neighbor. The struggle for survival is a struggle for reproduction. Survival of the fittest means survival of the survivors. No other fitness is measured. Darwin looks back over the bloody record, assumes without question that the process which has led to man must be good. "It may be said," he observes, "that natural selection is daily and hourly scrutinizing, throughout the world, the slightest variations; rejecting those that are bad, preserving and adding up all that are good; silently and invisibly working, whenever and wherever opportunity offers, at the improvement of each organic being. . . ." We are the survivors. Our predecessors line up behind us in unbroken file for billions of years. At every step they were threatened by other forms of life for which they, our ancestors, were food supply. Every random change in the genetic code meant new peril and new opportunity. Countless forms have perished in our jaws, in our claws, now in our hands. We are the survivors.

In the line of which we are the current issue the cumulative effect of mutation within a process of reproductive competition has been a brain capable of reason, of language, of scientific method. Such a brain has proven enormously advantageous in the struggle to reproduce. We now eat any form of life that suits our palate—at our pleasure, without danger of reprisal, as much as we want, until, if we choose, it is all gone. We have no rivals, the struggle is over. We are lords and possessors of the earth. But we did not get here by being gentle. We are extremely dangerous. We have nothing to fear but ourselves. We have much to fear.

To worship spirit is to worship that destructiveness which is part of spirit. Big fish eat little fish; big fish thereby increase in number while little fish tend to disappear, and presently there are not enough little fish left to satisfy the now numerous big fish. So one species of big fish will attack another, and the stronger and fiercer and perhaps crueler will prevail, will devour its neighbor, will grow stronger, more fierce, more cruel, and so will flourish, while its neighbor, diminished in number by these ever more successful forays, frightened, lonely, less able to find a mate, wanes and disappears.

This is the rule for the growth of spirit. Shall we worship? Shall we kneel to adore that breath of the universe which sweeps up to us from billions of years of such eatings and being eaten? Could there be another rule whereby spirit might go forward?

Man holds a mirror and spirit sees itself. For the first time spirit knows its face, sees itself in this man and that, the same spirit, in strong man and weak. All are bearers. Spirit rebels then against that rule that the strong shall destroy the weak whereby it has reached this far point at which to know itself, to view its course. Empathy appears. The order of march is changed. Spirit will continue along its ancient course the same upward journey, but with different rules: Thou shalt not kill, Thou shalt not bear false witness, Thou shalt love thy neighbor as thyself. The struggle for power will continue, for such is the means of progress, but within limits. Morality is born. The ascent of spirit, heretofore the thrust of blind purpose with method of gore, will henceforth proceed more decorously, with less spilling of blood, with deliberate restriction of means.

In some measure this vision has been realized. Within the several nations we live as a community, civil wars have become the exception, we do not come armed from our houses. We vie with our neighbor, outwit him, may starve him to death, but do not cut his throat. Let us praise moral progress. Spirit is ancient, has flourished on blood for billions of years; morality is an infant, has had but a few thousand in which to learn the ways, devices, whereby to direct the journey of spirit through the realm of man with less cruelty, with more compassion.

But could it be that man, recognizing spirit in others, exercising forbearance, creating morality, brotherhood—could it be that just here he ceases to be the advancing edge of spirit? Could it be that those rules whereby man determines that the continuing upward journey of spirit shall be infused with love halt the journey altogether? Could it be that the thrust of spirit leaps now from man to those aggregates of men, nations, which know not rules, which preserve in sovereignty the no-means-excluded struggle for power whereby spirit from the very beginning has advanced? Who is man, himself a latecomer, his civilization and morality later still, and still aborning, to make rules for universal spirit? Will spirit take heed? Or will we but legislate ourselves to some dark eddy, some back-looping current which spirit, unheeding, unhindered, will remorselessly rush by?

We like to believe that our brain has brought us into possession of a truth independent of our struggle to survive. But scientific method does not enable us to stand outside evolution. The mutations which led to a brain capable of divining the structure of the atom are tested in the same way as are all other accidents in the hereditary material. Not by grace or truth or beauty, but fruitfulness. It is our survival that vindicates the way we think, not the other way around. We would discard science for superstition were it advantageous, in the struggle to survive, to do so. In such circumstances, if we did not, those who lived by superstition would soon dominate the earth while those of us who remained loyal to reason would dwindle to the condition of Australian aborigines. We opt for nitrates over sacrifices because nitrates yield better crops. And for no other reason.

The brain capable of scientific method survives according to the rules whereby anything else survives, the advantage it conveys in the effort to extend life fruitfully into the future. The exploits of science dazzle us. We cure illness, move mountains, flash pictures around the world, fly to the moon. But the tale is not ended. We control enormous power, but with each gain in power we gain also in vulnerability. With each gain in knowledge we gain also in ignorance. We live now with new and desperate unknowns. We may or may not detonate so many hydrogen bombs, kill so many people, and so poison the air and oceans that human life will end. Were this to occur, and were there then anyone left in the midst of that universal desolation to reflect upon what had happened, he might be forced to conclude that those chance alterations in the germ-line which led to a brain capable of scientific method had proven in the long run to be unlucky, and that the roaches then proliferating over the devastated earth were, after all, the "fittest."

"The individual mind," writes Gregory Bateson, "is immanent but not only in the body. It is immanent also in pathways and messages outside the body; and there is a larger Mind of which the individual mind is only a sub-system." As Freudian psychology expanded mind inward to include unconscious processes, so Bateson would expand it outward through interconnected social and ecological systems. Both these changes reduce the scope of conscious self and suggest a certain humility; for this larger Mind of which we are a part, immanent throughout the universe, can be nothing other than God.

"If you put God outside," Bateson warns us, "and set him vis-à-vis his creation and if you have the idea that you are created in his image, you will logically and naturally see yourself as outside and against the things around you. And as you arrogate all mind to yourself, you will see the world around you as mindless and therefore not entitled to moral or ethical consideration. The environment will seem to be yours to exploit. Your survival unit will be you and your folks or conspecifies against the environment of other social units, other races, and the brutes and the vegetables.

"If this is your estimate of your relation to nature *and you have an advanced technology* . . . you will die either of the toxic by-products of your own hate, or, simply, of overpopulation and overgrazing. The raw materials of the world are finite."

We accomplish more than we intend. By social convention we postulate and define reality. Then we forget the convention, reality is just *out there.* We are gods, create a world, know not that we have authored all that splendor. Our knowledge-seeking activities, like the fingers of a blind sculptor examining his work, *discover* the configurations of a reality we have ourselves created and put there to be sought. It is the theory, said Einstein, which determines what we can observe. We create the nature and limits of reality, discover then the details assumed by that reality in accommodating itself to the shape we have given it.

How strange, the view of the world from the human heart—the pain, astonishment, mystery! How is it to be borne? What could redeem it?

"There are at work in us archaic forces," writes Norbert Bischof. "Structures older than we, older than mankind, grope for the world, dress it up the way they understand it, into a language of images, and derive joy and sadness from it—with the innocence and harmony of paradise. But our intellect, once created in a moment of arrogance, and since then spreading all-pervasively and irresistibly, now reaches out for this world of images, and with the superbright focus of better cognition tears to pieces its cozy duskiness. What if our intellect threatens to reveal to us a lunar landscape? What if all that it can show us is the face of death?"

Purpose gleams through the veil of history, the random throw of evolution. Acting in self-interest we bear spirit forward without our knowing or intending. Driven by ambition the scientist delivers his creativity to a spirit not his own. And that eternal fever in our flesh? From generation to generation spirit rides our lust while we go on miserably following our cocks thinking we succumb to private vices. Nations act in national interest, seize colonies, wage war, and inadvertently carry spirit forward.

Nothing, however, enables us to believe that *all* activities, either individual or social, serve spirit. For the movement of spirit is not uniform. Eddies swirl, currents flow backward, at times the river itself disappears in marsh or desert. A form of life which long has been the leading edge of advancing spirit may harden into its greatest obstacle.

The worship of spirit ascribes value to the means by which it was made, and if we look back we come sooner rather than later to conquest. If we find grandeur or holiness or beauty in a Parthenon, a Sermon on the Mount, a Mahler symphony, how can we disavow Pericles or Caesar or Napoleon? Can we believe that what we worship would have floated down to us on anything other than that river of blood? And have we not then arrived at Pope's "Whatever is, is right"?

"One thing, however," writes Jacob Burckhardt, "must be said of all great destructions: since we cannot fathom the economy of world history we never know what would have happened if some event, however terrible, had not occurred. Instead of one wave of history which we know, another, which we do not know, would have risen; instead of one evil oppressor, perhaps one still more evil."

Morality is meant to further the development of love and brotherhood, but may it not be that morality itself along with art and love and all those other flowers of spirit, grows from the bloodsoaked soil of a drive to power?

Hegel believed spirit to be autonomous, protected by God, proceeding invariantly upon ordained course. Freedom in this view belongs to God, man is simply used. Spirit therefore is safe, its progress guaranteed, man need do nothing but stand in awe. Alex-

ander and Napoleon, whipped on by private pas-
sions, serve unknowingly an ulterior cause. Morality
ministers to man's illusion of freedom and of responsibility, but is only shadow play; real causes move in
a different realm, are heedless of our guilt. There is
then, for those who achieve so grand a view, no occasion to moralize: whatever is, is right.

Two hundred years have passed and the world is
greatly changed. We have become, as Descartes
promised, lords and possessors of the earth. It is unclear whether we shall destroy it or preserve it, but
the enormity of our power is beyond doubt. We have
not now the confidence of Hegel. We find but a faltering progression of spirit, a contingent universe in
which anything may happen and all may be lost, in
which historical figures may or may not, and often do
not, serve spirit. An opposing tendency is afoot: as
spirit becomes conscious of itself the vessels of spirit
lose moderation, grow arrogant as well as drunk with
power.

No longer can we see man as a puppet jiggled by
a beneficent God. Freedom is concentrated in man;
God stands in awe of what we shall do. As the vessels
of spirit become more conscious and more powerful,
reaching in man an explosive acme of knowing and
of power, spirit becomes more vulnerable to its carriers. It has lost divine protection without gaining safe-
conduct from us who carry it forward. Man chooses,

may go this way or that, may worship spirit, move on in its ancient path, or may oppose it, deny it, perhaps destroy it utterly.

Spirit does not contend with freedom. We are as free as we are able to be, are dangerously free, and may in our arrogance destroy more than we can afford to lose. Nothing guarantees our progress or even our survival. Forms perish. Spirit does not require mankind. We now are the leading edge of spirit but nothing insures we shall so remain. The place of vision, the opportunity created by freedom, is so to live as to further the voyage of spirit, to remain its swiftest vessel.

The jungle, we say in our civilized arrogance, is lawless. Struggle is to the death; everything that grows and develops does so by killing something else which itself would want to grow and develop. Civilization invents morality, reduces this ruthlessness to a competition according to rules. Morality, that is to say, marks the advent of something radically new in the adventure of spirit: the attempt to continue according to law a journey which from the start has been lawless.

Spirit has come an enormous journey in darkness, blindly achieving ever-increasing form and awareness, leaping forward and upward with whatever force its leading vessel can command, ruthlessly discarding forms it has used and surpassed, catching a ride on whatever goes its way and goes the fastest, destroying anything that would stop or slow its going on. Living forms are transient vessels of something which passes through them and on, leaving them broken and forgotten, used—and used up—for a purpose not their own. The activities of these perished forms by which spirit so used them would seem to have served the individual purposes and the species purposes of these living things—to survive, to grow strong, to prevail—and so they did, so do they still, but behind these limited purposes, these ends in view, rides a larger purpose without end. The strong devour the weak, growth follows upon destruction, struggle is to death, and on the crest of this ceaseless wave of agony and triumph spirit is borne forward. Civilization, no more than thirty thousand years old, is but the latest moment in this long wash, and morality but the fledgling creation of that moment. With civilized man, for the first time ever, a living form decrees a change in the mode by which spirit shall advance. Morality is born of that moment in which spirit becomes aware of itself and aspires to direct its own future progress. It attempts to revoke the ruthlessness which heretofore has been the means of progress, and to continue that progress according to rules.

It is a grand view, but turns the truth around. Jungle and civilization are indeed opposed, but it is civilization that is lawless. Animals do not make rules, know not that they obey them, yet behave within the limits of what is permitted by norms inscribed in their nature. Only man denies the authority of such norms, declares that everything is permitted. Morality stands against this license but not, thus far, with great success.

Long did spirit live and move in the leaves of plants, in branches, in flowers. The movement of spirit is glacial. Animals seize for themselves a freedom unimaginable to plants, move about, roar, pounce, copulate. Their wanderings and their struggles conform to looser norms, but still conform; they wander within limits. Spirit rides their still lawful backs, and the movement of spirit is slow. During the span of man's time this movement becomes faster, most dizzyingly fast in the latest moment which is civilization.

Now arises a dark question. Could it be man's increasing lawlessness which yields this accelerating pace of upward-leaping spirit?

One by one and then in bunches, indiscriminately, have we challenged those traditional norms which limit what we may do. Ever faster do they fall, none now are left. Everything is permitted. Never has spirit been so free. Shall we get away with this arrogance? Do we overreach ourselves? Do we prepare in the atomic furnace of our Titans a great immolation? Perhaps spirit will be thrown back, will then once more move forward at a slower pace, borne by forms which know that some things are not permitted. And then? Will the whole tale be told again—and again, endlessly?

The end of certainty chastens morality. For what justifies violence is the certainty of being right. Having lost this certainty we must accept that we struggle toward provisional goods, oppose provisional evils. Because of this provisionality we should undertake to resist evil rather than to destroy it, to support the good rather than to instate it by murder. The absolute must take refuge in absolute modesty.

VI

THE FLAIL

DEATH is part of life. To live at all is to be doomed. But we have forgotten. There was a time behind our furthermost memory when life did not entail death. Let us rewind the tape.

The DNA molecule, coiled up within the nucleus of a single cell, is as long as a man is tall. In the generations behind us lie similar molecules of the same length, and behind them others, and so on and on. A hundred generations gives us six hundred feet of tape: Christ hangs on the Cross. We press the fast rewind, run it back a million years. Man is a new-comer on earth; the tape stretches endlessly behind him. At one hundred fifty million years we come to the origin of mammals. Tape still running smoothly, but the segments for each generation have become shorter. At two hundred seventy-five million years we see the first reptile, at three hundred million the first fish. At four hundred million years we arrive at the first flower. The tape is unbroken, but the individual segments have shrunk to a centimeter. This tape is finite. We hear a peculiar hum.

At a billion years in a warm ocean we come upon life without death. Each cell takes in nutriment, increases in size, divides in half, and then there are two. Not birth, but fission. Neither is parent and neither is child, neither is young and neither is old. These two cells then increase in size, then they divide; and so the generations succeed each other with neither youth nor age. Death is by misadventure. With a little luck one might live forever.

Yet it is not exactly a Golden Age. There is a certain dullness in the way they live. They don't gesture or touch, don't play games or give signals, don't fall in love. In solitary self-sufficiency each little organism sucks up what it needs from the surrounding fluid, elongates, pinches itself into two, and with each division the DNA molecule reproduces itself exactly. The tape of successive generations is not similar, but identical.

Now we run the tape forward a bit, watch the flickering succession, and presently we see something new. Two cells touch, a connecting tube is formed, a bit of substance exchanged. Life is beginning to create sex. For millions of years this intimate touching is sporadic, an optional method of reproduction, then is established as necessary and exclusive with organisms which now have become multicellular. They touch and intermingle, and from this mixing issues new life. Now the generations are not identical; for the single tape of the offspring, deriving from the two tapes of its predecessors, is not exactly like either one. Organisms differentiate, sexual identities appear. Male and female, in order to come together, must recognize each other, hence must give signals. Communication is born. There is proliferation of attributes and shifting of forms. By inventing sex, life has learned how to shake up hereditary traits like dice in a box, very special dice each of which bears a hundred thousand characters, and so has created an enormous capacity for change.

But among these fine fruits lies an asp. For now there is death. Not death by misadventure but by necessity. The tape itself is coded to destruct, and life, enriched by sex, is under sentence of death. We are conceived in close prison, wrote John Donne, and all our life is but a going out to the place of execution.

Valéry speaking beyond the grave to Rilke, recalling their last meeting at Muzot: ". . . a terribly lonely, very small chateau in a vast sad mountain region; old-fashioned, serious rooms with dark furniture, narrow windows: it constricted my heart. My imagination could not restrain itself in your rooms from eavesdropping on the endless monologue of a completely isolated soul with nothing to distract it from itself and from the consciousness of its uniqueness. A life so withdrawn seemed hardly possible to me, eternal winters long in such excessive intimacy with silence, so much space for dreams, so much freedom for the quintessential, the all too concentrated spirits which inhabit books, for the writer's fluctuating powers, for the forces of memory. Dear Rilke, you seemed to me locked up in pure time, and I feared for you the transparence of the too monotonous life which through the line of eternally similar days gives a clear view of death."

Friends die and the mystery envelops us. Something here calls for attention. With tenacious thought it might be grasped and understood. But from the nothingness toward which our lives are tending we are easily distracted. We lay it aside. Values are winnowed by bereavement and pain, by loneliness and guilt, but death is the ultimate flail. It may revoke any prior position on value, and it precludes any subsequent revision.

To see death clearly one may wait till one is dying, but to see life in the momentarily brilliant illumination of death one may not wait so long. For then fear supervenes. One dares not look, or else looks through blurred eyes and sees not what is there, but a landscape of longing. He who would see life clearly in its final illumination must invoke death early. When only a murmur is audible he must conjure the panic roar. From the serenity of the placid stream he must transport himself in imagination to the lip of the cataract. How then, looking back, seems the course of the river?

Friends die more frequently as we get older, and each death brings back the mystery, reminds us there is something here to be contemplated, some wisdom to be sifted from fear. But the empty heavens are too much, we turn away. There is so much to be done. We rush back to our problems, for the existence of problems affirms our existence. Unfinished business means that we, too, are unfinished. We lose ourselves in the daily round.

Then one day it's not someone else. The coronary occlusion is happening to the heart inside; the name on the report of malignancy is one's own. Then it's too late.

Eddie was lanky and twisted, had stringy black hair, a pasty face, and pale blue eyes, seemed about to dissolve and disappear into some wetness on the floor. He was stoop-shouldered, had a large Adam's apple, and seldom spoke. On that occasion, however, inspired by the sermon, "Death, the Door to Meaning," he ventured to speak.

"I gamble. Every week . . . Go to Stateline . . . or Reno . . . or Vegas. Usually drive my '57 Chevy.

Sometimes take my wife. Always know how much I can lose . . . usually twenty dollars . . . sometimes thirty. When I win, okay . . . When I lose, okay; I lose only what I can afford, what I decided on. But if I knew I would die in two weeks . . ." His eyes glistened. He choked, swallowed, coughed. ". . . I would . . . go a little harder. . . ." He squirmed, made an uncertain gesture with his right hand, looked up, his eyes grew teary, he waved, suddenly sat down, carried away by a vision of profligacy. We were amused, gave him a round of applause.

He asked me to go with him to Stateline, and for the first time did not take his careful allotment, but emptied his bank account—$198. We got to Harrah's in the evening, and I bought him a drink. I had slept most of the way because Eddie doesn't talk. I was getting bored, wished I hadn't come. At the crap table, without a tremor, Eddie put all $198 on boxcars —at thirty to one. The croupier thought it was a mistake, was trying to talk him out of it when Eddie calmly borrowed two dollars from me to make it an even two hundred, the house limit. The lady with the dice said, "Oh no, not me, I'm not going to roll!" Next was a kid in jeans who needed a shave; he was willing, blew on the dice, and rolled. And there they were, two sixes. Such a shout you've never heard, bells ringing, the manager came running. Eddie had won $6000 on one throw—and didn't turn a hair.

He was magic in that club. People crowded around him, touched him, particularly girls. It was not the money but something more thrilling, that here was a man with death looking over his shoulder. We had a hell of a weekend and the money was gone by Monday, but the girls still pressed around because they knew he was a man alive.

Three weeks later he came out of Harrah's at four in the morning with $37,000, was mugged in the entrance but broke away and got to the middle of the road before they cut him down. Three men snatched up his money and fled while he died there in the middle of Route 50 with the moon looking down.

Horace: "There were brave men before Agamemnon, many; but all alike, unwept and unknown, lie pressed by eternal darkness for lack of a sacred poet."

This clinging to uniqueness, which I have been viewing as an infirmity, is coming to seem necessary to the human condition. Being human starts with the consciousness of a unique self. To affirm one's self is to affirm this uniqueness. And if I do not affirm myself I cannot meaningfully affirm anything. But uniqueness entails the awareness of boundaries between self and not self; so to affirm self is to accept alienation. Alienation brings into life the experience of death; so the affirmation of self entails the affirmation of death. This is the trap: to cling to life drives one toward death, and there is no way to avoid anything of death without giving up something of life. An animal may live without the experience of death; but as life enlarges, death enters, and with each gain in awareness death enters more intimately into life. Against this encroachment of the void I advance a passionate desire that my uniqueness be recognized. Only then could that which is most essential to me be affirmed and preserved.

Marcel Proust carved this fluid and perishable stuff into the stone of literary accomplishment and it endures. But over the world ten thousand men died today, and each of them remembered the taste of little cakes in childhood, a taste from which associations radiated, for each of them as for Proust, encompassing all of life. With each of these deaths there was lost today an account of passion and courage and fear and cruelty of just such intricacy and length and singularity as Proust made permanent.

No, not permanent. Stone wears away, and who will read Proust in a thousand years? And what's a thousand years to the appetite for immortality? Having lost the eternity God once promised us why should we get excited by a millennium? There's no end to this hunger for the little cakes of eternal life, and no solution, and anyway if this conflict were resolved another would appear to take its place. Always there is something left over. It's hard to give up the idea of getting things settled once and for all, yet that idea defines death. So I should draw some comfort from conflict: as long as the problem isn't finished I'm not finished either.

Suddenly, as we walk, my wife's hand pushes its way into mine like a tiny frightened animal seeking shelter. "I've been thinking," she says, "over and over—it's such a trite thought—we've lived together so long . . . then one day one of us will die, and . . . will never see the other any more." She lives in others, ascribes nothing worthy of immortality to the isolated self even if that self be her own.

How brief and fitful our time.

In November Aunt Nell would wander among the elm trees, her hair a bone-whiteness against the black trunks. She would pick up the scarlet and yellow leaves, let them fall through her fingers. Children would cluster round her. "What are you looking for?" they would ask. "I'm admiring the brush strokes of God," she would say. The children would look up at her remote face, and beyond at the leafless branches swaying in the wind.

One day, suddenly restless, she wandered about the house, could not stop talking, said she had many things to do, that I must help her. She was looking for something, could not remember what. She sat down in front of me, leaned forward urgently, took my hands, pressed them tremblingly. Her own hands were gaunt and deeply hollowed; black serpentine veins stood out in high relief. Her skin was but a thin film with brown blotches. "Help me find it!" she exclaimed. A shudder passed across the frail body, her eyes became vacant.

After that she was always forgetting what she was starting to do. She wrote cryptic notes, would leave them about the house, but on finding them could not recall of what they were meant to remind her. She began to see strangers in her room. Always a lady, she never raised her voice, never spoke with other than utmost courtesy. One day, standing outside her bathroom, I heard her say in tones of appalling sincerity, "I beg of you, sir, I urgently *beg* of you, *do* allow me some privacy!" One night, fleeing some such tormentor, she fell down the stairs, broke both legs. Thereafter she was confined to bed. When I sat with her she would glance discreetly around the room which to me was empty but to her peopled. She said little because, I think, she thought it rude to converse in the presence of those others. She held my hands tightly. One day as I was leaving she asked me to lean over, brought her lips to my ear, whispered, "I'm sorry I can't introduce you. I don't know their *names!*" She developed pneumonia, then a urinary obstruction, had to be catherized. "My dear," she whispered, glancing about in an exhaustion of terror, "when will I ever see you alone?" One day in March as I was helping her sit up, a shudder rippled across her face as over the high branches of an elm at the first deep cut of an ax below. She turned her head toward the window and the sound of the wind. "Why did you turn off the light?" she said. Her hands shook, she would not lie down, was trying to escape something, pulling on me to get out of bed. Then the ax fell again and she cried out, her face suffused with dark color. Once more and then she was still.

After some weeks I began to go through her belongings. All was a jumble, many things had tags: a ring with a loose stone, "To be fixed"; a bundle of letters, "Uncle Henry writing from Lee's army"; a locket with a wisp of hair, "broken clasp"; a box of photographs, "To be sorted"; a bottle of ink, empty but for a hard residue, "Dried up." Everything was unfinished, nothing had come to conclusion. She had simply stopped like a clock at twenty past three. Nor would more time have made any difference; her life, broken off at eighty-two, would have been just as unfinished at ninety. To the universal spirit rushing through the generations of men it was properly over, the seed had been passed on; but in the plan of her life nothing was finished, the game was called because of darkness.

In my youth billboards sounded a warning: "Coming events cast their shadows before," and pictured a young man casting the shadow of a man with a paunch and a double chin. The death of Aunt Nell casts the shadow of my death, and these bits and pieces of unfinished business which seemed so important to her, to me so trivial and pathetic, prefigure the scraps of my life and how they will seem to someone whose duty it will be to go through them and make disposition. All the things I now struggle with, anguish over, upon which I try to impose order —might I not, right now, just as well tag them "Dried up, useless," and lay them aside?

The billboards had a ready formula whereby to avoid the foreshadowed fate: "Reach for a Lucky instead of a sweet." But where is the remedy for that unfinishedness foreshadowed for me? I look at Aunt Nell's leavings which I have piled up on her desk, and it is only my knowing how she worried over these things that moves me to take them seriously, to handle them with respect. For all their intrinsic worth I could sweep them pell mell away. And from this jaundiced distance I see my leavings in just such a heap on someone's desk some day to come.

How tie them up? How consume them utterly in a flame of living? How live so that the symphonic complexity of life end on a resolving chord?

The candle lies in its box in the cupboard. A woman lies abed, listens to the rain. The castle is empty. She gets up, shakes out her long black hair. Delicate feet in sandals follow each other, slowly, on black and white parquetry down a long gallery. She opens the cupboard, takes the candle, returns to bed. Rain throbs against leaded windows. Light and life are locked in the candle, but the key is not yet and the candle knows nothing. Delicate feet in sandals follow each other, quickly, over black and white parquetry down the long gallery. She looks up guiltily at ancestral portraits. The candle is returned to the cupboard.

Days pass, months, winter with its snows, spring flowers, summer, and now a cold wind drives scarlet leaves across the garden, whines over gray parapets. Again the woman opens the cupboard, takes the candle, places it in a silver holder on a damask table. Night falls, guests arrive, the match is struck. Key turns, the candle comes to life. Far above, faintly, dark rafters come into focus. The candle sees flowers, crystal, china, food, hears conversation, is awed by the dark-haired woman with smiling mouth but knows not of shared intimacy. Consciousness expands and now the candle sees itself reflected in a wine glass, is delighted by the delicate shape of its dancing spirit; now with horror sees itself shrinking. What happens? Whither does it go? It looks up frantically. It is disappearing into thin air against the dark rafters. Shrinking, shrinking, nothing avails. Was consciousness bestowed but that it might see the approach of death? It flickers, struggles, and is gone.

In the long dark at either end of brief awareness who has held us in hand? To what end? To whose hand go we now?

Life binds as a close cell, shrinking ever towards a coffin. Everywhere necessity waits. Nowhere the path to freedom, every door opens on duty. Situations require and I respond. I do what is right, a workhorse plodding faithfully, day after day, down the same furrow to the same end. On my way to the grave, serving purposes not my own.

I feel a sudden rebellion. In quest of lawlessness I take a plane to Rio, stay at a lavish hotel on the beach. My room is in the sky, to the east the sea, to the west the jungle. I sit availably in the bars, stroll the lounges, loll at the pool. To beautiful women I indicate attraction; to men of sinister bearing, gun runners perhaps, I offer conversation. Everyone treats me with politeness and reserve. I find no orgies, encounter no plots. I return to my room in the sky, a new cell in the same prison.

The next day I walk inland. I come to a meadow, sit in tall unfamiliar grass. There is no sun, the sky is a vast upturned dish. Presently I hear voices, turn to see children coming toward me. They walk abreast a few paces apart, form a long wavering line. Some hold hands, some are singing, one is followed by a

pony, a ball is being thrown back and forth, one flies
a kite. I stand in astonishment. They nod at me and
pass on without pause. A little girl with dark curls and
a sweet smile gives me a flower. I watch them disappear to the west; their voices become fainter, soon
are lost. The flower in my hand yields a heavy sweet-
ness; I feel longing, want to be with them. I set out
after them, walk faster, soon am running, but find no
one. After a while, exhausted, I give up and turn
back, encounter then a similar line of young men and
women. They pass around me with hardly a glance,
absorbed in themselves. Their riches of sexuality agi-
tate me, and I go on bitterly to my elegant hotel of
polite and unreachable people, to my solitary
confinement.

The next day I return to the meadow. I want to see
the children again. The high grass sways around me,
seed dropping. The sky again is leaden gray with
low-lying black clouds. I wait a long time, am dozing
when I hear the happy voices. Just like yesterday, in
a long line abreast, they come toward me laughing
and singing. Friendly greetings as they pass around
me and go on. I search among them for the girl with
dark ringlets, do not find her, follow them but can't
keep up. They go strangely fast. I call to them but
they do not pause. The distance between us increases. I run, gasp for breath, plunge on, it seems for
hours, and far ahead, faintly, I still can see them.

Apparently their pace slackens, for a time comes when I can walk and still keep them in view, indeed am coming closer. Now I see that these are not children but adults. They do not hold hands, do not laugh and sing. They have white hair, the men carry canes. They are serious, intent on some goal, plod on grimly. I am bewildered, am looking at them closely, trying to recall the children, when I notice that they are getting shorter. The day is getting darker, I cannot see their feet, their legs are disappearing, they are sinking into the earth. As I watch they vanish altogether. The sky is black. Before me I see nothing.

Desperately I try to find my way back. Again I am running, hour after hour, again I encounter coming toward me a group of young people. I pass them without pause, without looking. My chest writhes in pain. On, on I run. I think now I hear the sound of the sea. Far ahead, coming toward me, a line of children abreast. I veer around them. As if pursued I flee. At the hotel I pack immediately, catch a plane for home.

The laughing girl in the bikini under the red and blue umbrella, the willowy girl with the doe eyes and generous mouth at the cocktail party—crystallization points of a passionate preoccupation. Of what nature? Not a vision of giving, of coming to know the needs of such a girl and of meeting those needs.

THE FLAIL

That's what love is and is no part of this wild yearning. I'm concerned with getting. What do I want?

Whatever it is I must give up hope, must try to want to give. But I wish I knew what it is I want, so deeply, so vainly, before I give up wanting it.

Much high-flown untruth is written about love by able and serious writers. Feeling obliged to assert a norm of propriety, they falsify what they know. The definitions of mature love at which they arrive do not describe what goes on in the hearts of mature men.

The craving becomes more frantic, grasping, as one gets older. It's time to give it up, this longing for roundness and fullness, for the sweet breasts, the fresh smile. Old men in the Tenderloin still chase after it. Spare me their grotesqueries. It is time to yearn no more, to leave to the young this hungering. I don't want to be pushed out of life, kicking, like a child in a tantrum, or dragged by the heels to the firing squad. I want to walk out, detached and unafraid.

The only thing in life worth having is not a thing, not even a category of things, but a feeling: a soaring, intense, exalted longing. It comes on without cause, but is rare and is easily dispelled by pettiness or anger. It is a feeling infinitely tender, yet exhilarating —as when the young lovers come running down the long windswept quay in *The Cranes Are Flying*—a flowing out of one's self into others, intense joy yet without fear of death, for one is fused with others and boundaries vanish. It is hope and beauty and love and selflessness. It stands in contrast to that other feeling I know so well, the aching woman-hunger, the greediness to conquer and penetrate, which is sad and bitter and hopeless, which is a whining, "Come love me, stimulate me with something new, minister to my emptiness, feed me," and comes on when one has given up the effort to make something new, to give.

Nobility ventures all in uncertainty and risk, reaches out to help, not from a position of strength, but precisely when mired in weakness and absurdity.

VII

THE MAN
OF REASON

B EHOLD the man of reason. Regard him in his work. He has struggled with this problem all his life. Solve it here in one guise and it appears there in another, as if a different problem. He is nearing sixty when he understands finally its true and single nature: not knowing how to live.

Such an insight, you might think, would cast him down, but he feels hope, exhilaration. It's better, he thinks, to have one big problem than a bagful of small ones. You can concentrate your efforts, create a single strategy. How, then, does one learn how to live? One must search, see what can be seen, analyze, make connections, relate things to each other in causal sequences. For a rational man there is no other way than the way of intelligence to learn anything. But in learning how to live, intellect is treacherous, for life is a matter of rhythms while intellect reduces rhythms to law.

He goes back to Hegel, to Nietzsche, to the pragmatists, the positivists, the dialectical materialists, ransacks the old closet of philosophy, fumbles around there in the dark as he has so often in the past, but now with a clearer sense of what he is looking for. He goes back to the poets, to the *Elegies* and the letters of Rilke, the effete but ruthlessly honest meditations of Eliot; returns to the searchers after God: Pascal, Kierkegaard, Teilhard de Chardin. He has learned nothing, is still the student, a doomed centipede unable to correlate all those legs, falling down, getting up, trying again, always signing up for another course: "The Anatomy of Legs," "Legs, their Physiology and Biochemistry," "Advanced Leg Dynamics," and now, still hoping, a yet more advanced course—"How to Walk." All these courses have in common the method of intelligence: they take the problem apart, carefully, piece by piece, seeking hidden relationships. He hopes to find the rhythm by dismantling the melody, examining each beat separately.

Look at him, age sixteen, at a high school dance, already a master of this methodology. With great yearning he watches the dancers, remains aloof. Cautiously he moves along the wall, simulates nonchalance, as if at home in such gatherings. He smiles, nods, leans against a door, and, having been shown in a thousand advertisements the connection between poise and smoking, lights a cigarette. He feels dizzy, coughs, moves on, chats with a teacher, makes it appear he is taking but a brief break from the dancing. In fact he is watching the dancing feet. How is it done? What is the formula? He is diagramming the movement. What is the excursion of each foot? How far? In what direction? What sequence? Now he looks at the faces of the girls. How do you tell which one, on being asked, will say yes? What is the formula for that?

Suddenly before him is a girl with dark flowing hair and smiling eyes, and with every beat of the music her body registers a slight response, a resonance, which wants to become a full participation. Along his sides the trickle of sweat, the smell of fear. "Hello, Jan," he says. His mouth is paper-dry, he swallows, waves a hand casually toward the dancers. "Reminds me of that scene in *Gatsby*, the summer night, couples swaying under the paper lanterns, and that *marvelous* line '. . . old men pushing young girls backward in eternal graceless circles.'" He nods, moves on; and Jan, who sailed into his life like a comet, trailing glittering promise, is swept away, lost.

My whole life has been given over to this search and I have found nothing. I'm growing old and still know not how to live. It's already too late to do much with the answer, which, in any event, seems still remote.

One day, though, I shall have it. An intimation of final justice tells me this quest shall not have been in vain. Like the tourist who, avid to buy, receives his letter of credit only as he is departing the country of bargains, I shall be unable to use it, but will count it a victory in principle.

It comes to me suddenly that I don't want to go on looking. This has been true, I now think, for quite a while though I'm just now realizing it. I've been telling myself I'm just not in the mood, lack inspiration, don't know which way to turn, can't settle on how to proceed; but these are rationalizations. I *can* continue. I *do* have ideas, nothing halts me but lack of will.

I'm sick of searching. Something in me recoils. Being so futile the quest seems pretentious. I am humiliated by the triviality of what I accomplish—notes from a bottle—feel exposed in a foolish grandiosity, like a lover who, in a flight of romantic eloquence, is told he has bad breath. I see myself as a solemn and unwitting clown, have no heart for picking myself up, brushing my teeth, and trying again. I have crawled into the bush like a wounded animal, have remained unaware of this withdrawal because of the importance to me of concealing hurt, even from myself. I don't cry, don't complain, but take it like a man —stiff upper lip, stiff lower lip, stiff smile, stiff shrug, and on with the quest for how to live. But the wound is bleeding. I'm dragging. Only in appearance do I carry on. I accomplish nothing, am falling by the way.

There are limits to will, and this exceeds these limits. I must not force this issue, must give myself time to recover. I want simply to live. I yearn for the unexamined life.

The rebel conforms, unwitting, to an ulterior authority. Trampling the flag and setting out on a course, as it seems, of radical freedom, he meekly obeys a law he knows not of. Shouting down the official music, he does his little dance to an unheard tune, falls away into the common void, obedient as the rest of us.

I feel a web of puppet strings across my face, my voice has a dying fall. I shan't be long.

Betrayed by transcendence, we return to the present. We look around, we touch, we taste, we feel. Presently we begin to say, "This is better than that." We value it, we want to hold on to it, point it out to others, and almost at once there's a trying to create, to contribute, a drive for transcendence which leads us to betray the present, commit our energies to the future. Love of the present leads us to betray the present; the effort to hold something forever leads us to lose even that moment of possession we might otherwise have.

It is not the disorder and confusion of the marketplace which drives me to the mountaintop; it's my delight in the marketplace that impels me to desert it. Love of life leads me to betray life; love of the actual sends me searching after the ideal; love of the present leads to the sacrifice of the present to a future that never comes.

My daughter throws a ball for her dog. Out of the trees, suddenly, comes a large yellow dog, attacks, is tearing at her dog. She weeps desperately. The violence and the tears are everywhere, behind a tree, beneath a leaf, in the smiles of a summer day. Escape, forget for a while, but not for long. I separate the dogs and her sobs diminish, but one day it will be me, or someone else dear to her, and she'll be sobbing again in just such helplessness. Our safe world may be lost in the spite, the vanity, the self-indulgent fit of one tyrant, and the sobbing children of Vietnam, the screaming mothers, will be all around us. The crazy violence that is everywhere, promiscuous, flares up in an instant, with no more warning, no more meaning, no more reason than a dogfight. How little time for laughter, how brief our innocence of what lies in wait.

What can I do with what I know? What is my task?

THE MAN OF REASON

Am sinking, sinking. Black mire rises about my face. The unexamined life is strangling me. Can't write, can't read, soon perhaps will be unable to listen to music. Behold the man of reason. He has followed the straight line of logic to the very end where it twists back upon him in a manacling snarl. Has he nothing to say on this, the day of the fighting dogs?

If despair can move me to resume the search perhaps my time is soon.

My wife has built for me a new study. Blue ceiling, birch walls, wonderful smell of new lumber. I feel a deepening intolerance of apathy, of not making anything, am sliding downhill on an old life that is really over.

"You won't find much jesting at scars among the morning walking wounded," says F. P. Tullius.

He who has a message, who deals in salvation, writes a book of structured argument, of hierarchic order, of reasons in sequence. Not I. My life is all searching, never finding. I bear witness to what I have seen—a maze of roads, conflicting signs, freeways that end on nowhere, angelic maidens who fall under a spell and turn drab, far-reaching insights which become inert and explain nothing, blueprints of reason which twist out of shape and vanish with a twang in a minor key. Mine can be but a book of episodic thought and feverish vision. I aim, not to persuade, but to intone.

Sometimes sitting alone in my new study, among familiar and beautiful things, lost in thought, looking out the window at a cold sky, at motionless trees, I turn an inner corner, vaguely familiar, and all at once am at the edge of such despair the only mystery is that I'm still here, a survivor, in this strange land.

Whenever I think "I don't know what to write," I must stop, make the correction: "I don't know *how* to write it." For the "what" is given, is what I most deeply feel, is this despair, lodged there in me. How get at it, how make it the object of creation?

We are defeated in work and in love, but keep going. Though now we know the defeat to be in the nature of things and so unavoidable, we keep trying, hoping still to achieve when all hope has gone an unexpected victory, perhaps a moment of glory.

I have always been too guilty to be happy. Guilt such as mine threatens life itself. The first task, there-fore—and never has there been time for a second—is to fend off an inner accusation that threatens to annihilate. This I have done, by work, day after day after day, and so life has passed, and looking back I can see I've fought my demons to a draw, or a little better, but where, lost to me, was the music, the laughing in the night?

Whenever I say, "I hate that person," then, however despicable his behavior, it is my own consciousness which is filling up with hate, as a crystal vase may be filled with mud. Take care. Preserve the transparence. Time is running out. Better look over meanness until gaze alights on goodness.

I smell my death on the wind, want to see something of beauty and nobility in the time that is left, to enlarge consciousness.

This desert will not negotiate, is fevered and desperate, sand whispers an ultimatum: destroy awareness with death-seeking diversions or elevate it by continuing the search. Maybe I can never resolve this, will forever be bouncing between the devil and God. Maybe I should simply take it as my fate, accept the derisive arrows of emptiness, the winters of destruction, search when I can.

I adjure myself: stay with the main show, do not be drawn off into side shows, diversions, entertainments. Do only what you are most solemnly charged to do. Whatever is elective is a turning away. There in the big top a man is hanging by his teeth, twisting, spinning, spotlights playing over him, the drums beginning to roll. He's going to fall and nothing can be done, no net, but in the moments remaining he may yet achieve something remarkable, some glittering stunt, a movement perhaps of breathtaking beauty.

The main show is the search. It mounts on despair,

spins there above you. Any turning away to watch the dancing bears is a betrayal of the dangling man. Hold fast, stay with him, watch the twists and turns of his brief agony, study his condition. What in this fateful moment can he still do? This is your task, to observe and make your report.

Is it not time? Whom do I address? I have reached that nadir for which there is not enough distraction within the limits of destructiveness I can permit myself and still live. It is time to take up again the seeking out of those faint footprints in the night, to try again, perhaps to hope again, and, beyond the trying, to seek the means to keep on seeking when nothing is found.

Sometimes I—even I!—feel a wild and deep joyousness, the exaltation of cold wind on one's face when one is young.